OWL GIRL

Published in 2018 by Hare Brand Ideas, Swannanoa, NC 28778 USA
Written and Illustrated by Jerald Pope

ISBN: 978-0-9975582-4-1

Printed in USA
75 pages

To comment, compliment, complain, or delve further into the artistic ouvre of Jerald Pope, visit hare-brandideas.com

 Much Thanks to: Bette Bates, David Billstrom, The Black Mountain Public Library, Cecil Bothwell, Ursula Goebels-Ellis, Ann Kirschner, Niko Kwiatkowski, Mary Lounsbury, Teresa Luckman, Madeleine Pope, Sal D'Angio, Sue Westmoreland, Julie Williams

Extra Much thanks to Alex Alford

OWL GIRL
BY
JERALD POPE

FOR
REBECCA

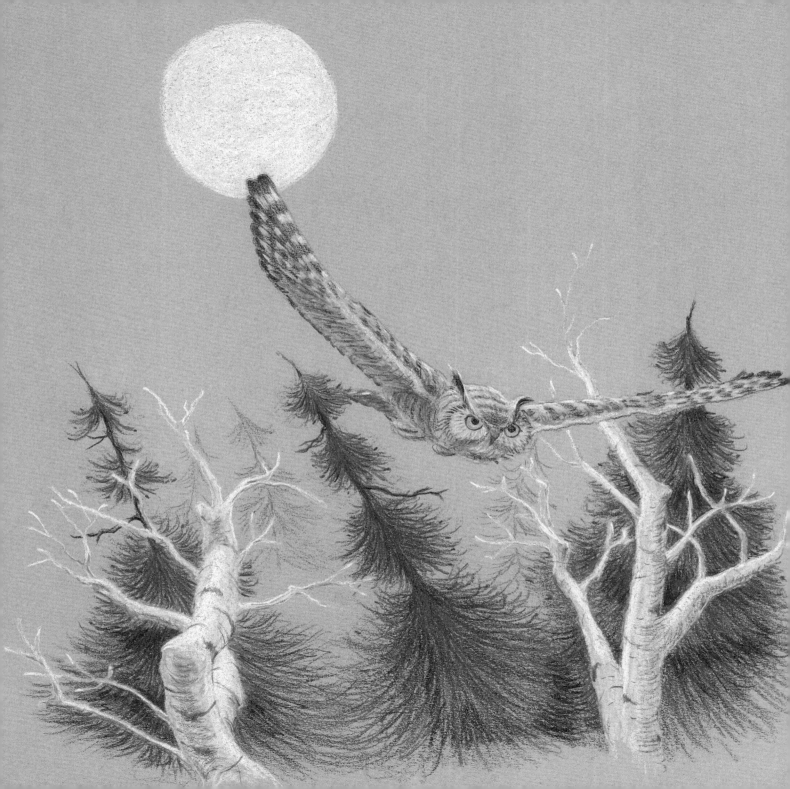

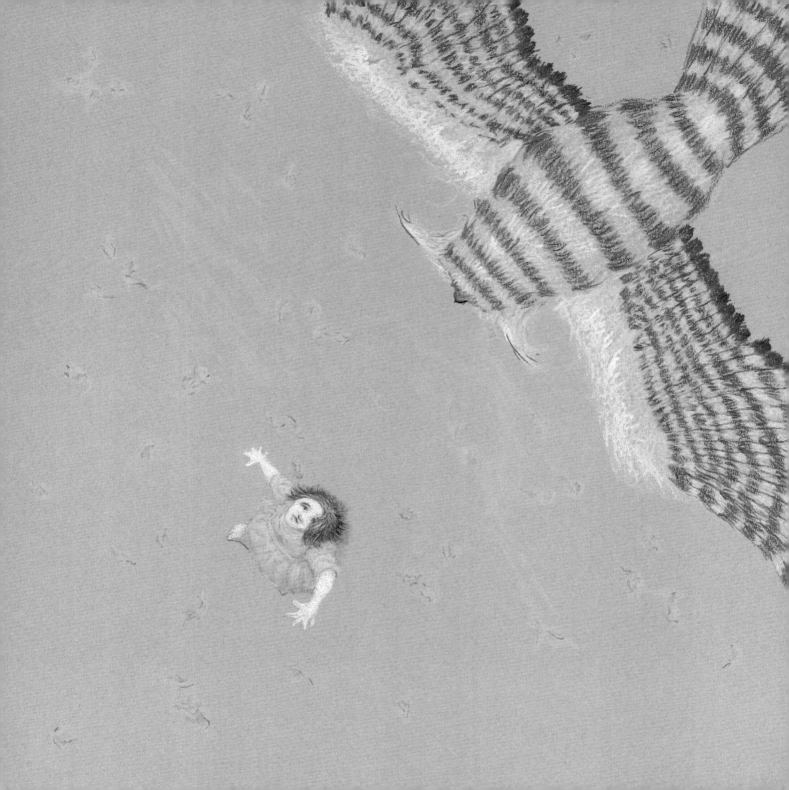

Made in the USA
Columbia, SC
12 November 2018